The Smi... Buddha

Heinemann English Language Teaching
A division of Reed Educational and Professional Publishing Limited
Halley Court, Jordan Hill, Oxford OX2 8EJ

OXFORD   MADRID   FLORENCE   ATHENS   PRAGUE
SÃO PAULO   MEXICO CITY   CHICAGO
PORTSMOUTH (NH)   TOKYO   SINGAPORE
KUALA LUMPUR   MELBOURNE   AUCKLAND
JOHANNESBURG   IBADAN   GABORONE

ISBN 0 435 27768 5

This reader is also available on cassette
ISBN 0 435 27818 5

Designed by David Brancaleone
Illustrations by David Mitcheson
Cover illustration by Cathie Felstead

Heinemann New Wave Readers

Series Editor: Alan C. McLean

Level 3

Murder at Mortlock Hall by Donald Dallas
Sheela and the Robbers by John Escott
Dancing Shoes by Colin Granger
One Pair of Eyes by Caroline Laidlaw
Born to Run by Alan C. McLean
The Smiling Buddha by Michael Palmer

Filmset by Crawley Composition Ltd
Printed in Malta by Interprint Limited

96   97   98   10   9   8

Michael Palmer

The Smiling Buddha

HEINEMANN NEW WAVE READERS

1 My first day in Thailand

I like Thailand. It's different. I like the country. I like the people. I like the temples too. There are temples everywhere. They're quiet, peaceful places. And they're full of beautiful things.

On my first day in Thailand I visited a temple. A temple on a hill. I met a Thai girl there. She was very friendly. She asked me a lot of questions about myself.

'What's your name?' she asked.

'My name's Gordon – Gordon Taylor,' I said. 'But my friends call me Tinker.'

'Where are you from, Tinker?'

'I'm from Australia.'

'What do you do there?'

'I'm a writer. I'm an artist too,' I told the girl. 'I write stories and I draw the pictures for them.'

'That's interesting,' she said. 'I studied art at university. Now I work for the Thai government. I work for the Fine Arts Department.'

'What's your name?' I asked her.

'Supaporn,' the girl said.

'Can I call you Sue?'

'Yes. Of course.'

'I'm interested in Thai art,' I told Sue. 'I like these Buddhas. They're beautiful. Are they very old?'

'These Buddhas here aren't very old,' Sue said. 'But there's an old Buddha over there. It's behind those rocks. It's very beautiful. Come and see it.'

Then I heard a loud voice behind me. 'Hey! Wait for me. Can I come with you?'

I looked round. There was a man behind me. He was a big man. He had a big cigar in his hand and a big smile on his face.

'Hi!' he said. 'My name's Bud.'

'I'm interested in Buddhas too,' Bud said. 'I collect them. My house is full of Buddhas. My friends call them "Bud's Buddhas". Let's go and have a look at this Buddha.'

Sue walked towards the rocks at the back of the temple. Bud followed her. I followed him.

I looked between the rocks and saw a dark hole. A cave. There was something in the cave. But I couldn't see it very clearly.

'Is that the old Buddha?' Bud asked.

'No,' said Sue. 'That's not a Buddha. That's a priest. We must be very quiet. Wait here.'

7

After a few minutes the priest came out of the cave.

'Hi!' said Bud. 'Can we go in there and see your old Buddha now?'

'No,' said the priest. 'I'm sorry. You can't.'

'Why not?'

'Because the Buddha's not there. Someone took it last night. Someone came in the middle of the night and stole it!'

Sue looked at me sadly. 'There are a lot of bad people in our country now,' she said. 'Temple robbers. They steal things from our temples. Old things. Beautiful things. They sell them to people from other countries.'

'That stolen Buddha is worth a lot of money,' said the priest. 'It's very old.'

'Can't the police catch these men?' I asked.

'They try to catch them,' said Sue. 'And the Fine Arts Department is helping the police to find them. But it isn't easy.'

'I'll help too,' I said. 'I'll look for the stolen Buddha. I'll keep my eyes open. And my ears too.'

'Thank you,' said Sue. 'Here's my telephone number.'

She wrote a telephone number on a piece of paper and gave it to me.

'I'll keep my eyes open for your Buddha too,' Bud said with a smile.

I didn't like his smile.

'Now I must go to the police station,' said Sue. 'Goodbye. I hope we'll meet again.'

'I hope so too,' I said.

9

I walked down to the beach. The sand was hot and the sea was warm. But there was a cool wind. I felt happy.

I looked up at the sky. It was all blue. I looked out to sea. The sea was blue too. And green. And I could see a small island out there. A long way out.

Not far from the island there was a beautiful boat. A rich man's yacht. 'Maybe it's Bud's yacht,' I thought.

I looked back at the beach and saw Bud. He was in a restaurant under the palm trees. He was with a man. The two men shook hands. Then Bud came out of the restaurant and got into a speedboat.

The boat was small but it was very fast. It drew a white line across the water to the beautiful yacht near the island.

'Yes,' I thought. 'That is Bud's yacht. Bud's a very rich man. That yacht is like a hotel.'

'I don't need a hotel,' I thought. 'But where can I sleep tonight?'

I looked at the restaurant again. There were little wooden houses all round it. Holiday bungalows. They were like Thai houses. But they weren't for Thai people. They were for tourists.

The bungalows looked interesting. And they looked cheap.

I walked to the restaurant. The name LEE'S CABANA was over the entrance.

Bud's friend came out of the restaurant. He had a big smile on his face. It was just like Bud's smile.

'Good morning,' Bud's friend said. 'Can I help you? Would you like to stay in one of my bungalows? They're very comfortable. And very cheap.'

10

'All right,' I said. 'I'll take one of your bungalows for tonight.' I paid the man the money.

The man was very friendly. He asked me a lot of questions about myself. 'What's your name? Where are you from? What do you do?'

'My name is Lee,' he told me. 'This is my restaurant. These are my bungalows. Come and see my shop.'

He took me into the room behind the restaurant. It was full of all kinds of things. Things for tourists.

'Do you want to buy any souvenirs?' Lee asked. 'We sell everything here.'

'Do you sell Buddhas? Old Buddhas?' I asked him.

Lee looked at me in a strange way. Then he smiled. 'No, I don't have any Buddhas in my shop. They cost a lot of money. And I don't want trouble with the police.'

I didn't sleep well that night. My bungalow was full of mosquitoes. My head was full of dreams. Bad dreams about Bud and his friend Lee.

I didn't like Bud and I didn't like Lee. I didn't like their smiles. They were friends. Did they work together? Did they steal Buddhas?

I got up early the next morning and went for a walk along the beach. I walked out into the warm water and watched the sun rise. The sun came up from behind the island like a big red football.

'That's a beautiful island,' I thought. 'I must paint it.'

13

I turned and walked back to the beach. There was a white boat on the sand. The name LEE'S CABANA was in big red letters on the side. The boat looked very fast. Why did Lee need a boat like that?

I looked through the window of the cabin. The cabin was dark inside, but I could see something in there. Something lying under a pile of clothes in the corner.

Was it a man? Was it the stolen Buddha?

Suddenly I heard a noise. I turned round and saw Lee.

'Good morning, Mr Tinker,' he said. 'You're up early this morning. Are you looking for something? Can I help you?'

This time Lee didn't smile. He didn't look very friendly. 'Ah, hello, Mr Lee,' I said, 'It's a beautiful morning, isn't it? I'm just looking at your boat. Can you take me out to that island? I want to paint it. I want to stay there for a night or two.'

'I'm sorry. You can't do that, Mr Tinker,' said Lee. 'There's no food on that island. There's no water.'

'I can take food and water with me.'

'No. You can't go to that island,' Lee said. 'I can't take you there in my boat. It needs a new engine. Look, there's the old engine under that pile of clothes.'

I looked through the window again. It wasn't the stolen Buddha. It was only an old engine. I was stupid.

'Now let's go back to the restaurant,' Lee said. 'What would you like for breakfast?'

After breakfast I went back to the beach. It was noisy there now. People were playing games on the sand. They were shouting and laughing. There was too much noise.

16

I sat on the sand and looked at the island. It was quiet and peaceful out there. No tourists. No shouting.

I lay down and thought about the island. I really wanted to go there. I wanted some peace and quiet. I wanted to paint and write. I wanted to be alone.

But I needed a boat to get to the island.

I closed my eyes and enjoyed the morning sunshine. It painted all kinds of colours inside my head.

'Hello, Tinker. What are you dreaming about?'

I opened my eyes quickly and saw Sue's face above me.

'I'm dreaming about you,' I said.

'Really?' Sue said with a smile. She had a beautiful smile.

'Yes. Really. I'm dreaming about you. And about Buddhas and Bud and that island out there. I want to stay there for a day or two. All alone. Like Robinson Crusoe.'

'Robinson Crusoe? Who's he?' asked Sue.

'Oh, he's just a man in a book. He lived on an island all alone for years and years,' I said. 'But I can't get to my island. I haven't got a boat.'

17

'I'll help you,' Sue said. 'My uncle's got a boat. It's only a little wooden boat, but you can get to your island in it. A lot of fishermen go to that island. It's called Crab Island.'

Sue took me along the beach to a little village. It was a fishing village. There were fish everywhere, on tables, drying in the sun. And the smell of fish was everywhere too.

There was a line of fishing boats on the beach. The colours were beautiful. Red, yellow and blue. I wanted to paint them. But I wanted to get to the island first.

Sue pointed to a big house at the back of the village.

'That's my uncle's house,' she said. 'Come and meet my uncle.'

Sue's uncle didn't speak English but he was very friendly and helpful. He showed us his boat. It didn't have an engine. Only a paddle.

'He says you can use his boat for a day or two,' Sue told me.

'Thank you,' I said. Then I got into the boat with Sue and I paddled it back to Lee's restaurant.

I pulled the boat up on to the beach and ran to my bungalow. Sue waited in the restaurant. I packed my bag. It didn't take long.

'You are in a hurry,' she said. 'Do you want to get away from me so quickly?'

Sue laughed and I laughed with her. Then I got into the boat and paddled out to sea.

'Good luck!' Sue shouted. She waved me goodbye. 'Take care.'

I paddled towards Crab Island. Out at sea the wind was strong and the waves were high. After a few minutes my boat was nearly full of water. I stopped and threw out some of the water.

Suddenly I heard a loud noise. The noise of a boat engine. It was one of the boats from the fishing village. A black boat with pictures of snakes and dragons on its sides. There was a big eye at the front.

A fisherman stood by the engine at the back of the boat. He had black trousers and his skin was nearly black too. He didn't look very friendly.

The fisherman pointed back to the beach. He waved his arms and shouted at me. *'Cabana! Lee!'*

'He wants me to go back,' I thought.

Then the fisherman turned his boat just in front of me. It made a big wave. My little boat was full of water again. I was frightened but I didn't want to go back.

After an hour I got to Crab Island. I pulled my boat up on the beach. It was a beautiful white beach with green palm trees at the back and green water in front. There were big rocks all around the beach.

Then I saw a cave in the rocks. 'That's my hotel for tonight,' I said to myself.

I put my bag in the cave. Then I lay down under a palm tree. I was very tired. I thought about Sue and Bud and Buddhas and a lot of other things.

Suddenly I heard a noise. I looked out to sea and saw the black fishing boat again. It came towards me very quickly. Its big white eye looked down on me.

The fisherman jumped out of the boat. He had something in his hand. It was like a big fork. Or a small

spear. He waved the spear at me. *'Boo!'* he said.

I was frightened. The fisherman had a spear. 'What is he going to do?' I asked myself.

'What do you want?' I asked. But the fisherman didn't understand. He turned and walked away.

After a few minutes the fisherman came back. He had a big bag in his hand. He opened the bag and showed me. It was full of crabs. *'Boo,'* he said. *'Lee! Cabana!'*

Then I understood. *Boo* was the Thai word for crab. The crabs were for Lee's restaurant.

The fisherman smiled and jumped back into his boat. He started the engine and turned his boat towards Lee's restaurant.

Soon I was alone again.

'I'm hungry,' I said to myself. 'I want some fish.'

I picked up a piece of wood from the beach and made a fishing spear. Then I swam out to sea with it.

There were some big rocks in the water not far from the beach. I stood on them and looked around. I could see Bud's big yacht. I could see the fisherman's boat too. It was on the beach in front of Lee's restaurant.

I dived from the rocks into the green water. Into a beautiful world. There were fish everywhere. All kinds of fish. The colours were fantastic.

I held my fishing spear in front of me and swam after one of the fish. It was blue and green, red and yellow . . . All the colours of the rainbow. A Rainbow Fish. It swam slowly in front of me, but I couldn't get close to it. I followed it down between the rocks.

Then I saw something really strange. I saw a man. A man sitting on the sea-bed. And there was a rope round his neck.

'My God!' I thought. 'A dead man. But how did he get there?'

Then I saw that it wasn't a man. It was a Buddha.
'Perhaps it's the stolen Buddha,' I said to myself.

I took the rope in my hands. It was tied to a rock. I followed the rope up to the surface of the water. Then I stood up on the rocks and pulled on the rope. It was hard work. But at last the Buddha came out of the water. It sat on the rocks beside me. The Buddha seemed to smile at me. I liked the Buddha's smile.

Then I heard a noise behind me. It was the fisherman's boat again. And Lee was in the boat with the fisherman.

'What are you doing with that Buddha, Mr Tinker?' asked Lee. 'Give it to me, please.'

'Why?' I asked. 'It isn't yours. It's from that temple on the hill, isn't it? Did you steal this Buddha?'

'Don't ask stupid questions, Mr Tinker,' Lee said.

He waved a big knife in front of my face. Then he smiled and picked up a fishing net from the front of the boat. He threw the fishing net over my head. There were heavy weights all round the bottom of the net. They pulled me down into the water.

'Goodbye, Mr Tinker.' Lee smiled again. 'You think you're a big fish, don't you? But there are a lot of other big fish in the sea. Perhaps you will meet some of them down there.'

I looked down into the deep, green water. I looked up at the blue sky and my beautiful green island.

Then the water closed over my head.

I tried to swim, but I couldn't move my arms. The net was too heavy. It pulled me down into the water, deeper and deeper.

I pulled at the net with my hands. I kicked at it with my feet. It caught on a sharp rock. I kicked again and again, harder and harder.

Suddenly the rock cut a big hole in the net. I pulled myself through the hole and swam up to the surface of the water. Back to the big rocks.

The Buddha was still there. But where was Lee?

Then I saw the fisherman's boat. And there was another boat behind it. A police boat.

Suddenly I heard a loud bang! A gun!

The two boats stopped. There was a lot of noise. Voices. Shouting. After a few minutes the boats turned and came towards me.

Lee was still in the fisherman's boat. There were two people in the police boat. One of them was Sue.

'Sue!' I shouted. 'What are you doing here?'

'We followed Mr Lee here,' Sue said. 'We wanted to talk to him about the stolen Buddha. But what have you got there?'

Lee answered. 'It's the Buddha from the hill temple.' He pointed at me. 'This man stole it. He's a temple robber.'

'I didn't steal this Buddha!' I shouted. 'I found it down there in the sea.'

'Really?' said Sue. 'And how did it get there?'

'I don't know. Perhaps Lee put it there,' I said. 'Maybe he wanted to sell it to Bud.'

'Who is Bud?' asked the policeman.

'He's Lee's friend,' I said. 'He collects Buddhas. That's his yacht over there.'

We all looked at Bud's yacht. We could see Bud. He got into his speedboat. He came straight towards us.

'Hi, everyone,' Bud said.

Then his eyes opened wide. 'What have you got there? Is that my Buddha?'

'Your Buddha?' said Sue.

'Well, it's not my Buddha yet. But I'm going to buy it. Mr Lee is going to sell it to me.'

'What are you talking about?' Lee asked.

'Remember? In your restaurant yesterday morning?' "Come to Crab Island at six o'clock," you said. "We can look at the Buddha there and talk about the price."'

'I didn't say that,' said Lee. He looked at Sue and the policeman. 'I don't know anything about this. I don't steal things.'

'No. But you buy and sell things,' said Sue. 'Perhaps other people steal things for you.'

Suddenly I understood everything. I turned to Sue. 'I know,' I said. 'Bud wanted an old Buddha. He told Lee. Lee told the fisherman. The fisherman stole the Buddha from the temple. He took the Buddha to the island and left it in the sea. Lee told Bud to meet him here. But then I arrived. The fisherman saw me. He told Lee and brought him here. Then . . .'

'Look out!' cried Sue.

Lee jumped up and ran along the boat towards me. He had a big knife in his hand. But the fisherman saved me. He kicked the knife out of Lee's hand. Then he kicked again. He kicked Lee on the side of the head.

Lee fell over the side of the boat and hit the water with a loud splash.

'Help!' Lee shouted. 'I can't swim.'

I looked at Sue again. 'He thinks he's a big fish,' I laughed. 'But he can't even swim!'

And that's really the end of the story. I was right about Lee and the fisherman. The fisherman took the Buddha from the temple. But it was Lee's idea. The fisherman told the police everything.

The next morning Sue and I went up to the temple on the hill. We took the Buddha with us and put it back in the cave. Then we sat outside the cave and listened to the priest.

'The fisherman is not really a bad man,' said the priest. 'He's a poor man. He needs money. Mr Bud is a rich man. He pays a lot of money for things like our Buddha. So sometimes poor people steal these things and sell them. They sell them to men like Mr Lee. Men like Mr Lee are bad men. They make a lot of money.'

'You're right,' said Sue. 'Lee is a bad man. He's in prison now. There were a lot of stolen things in his shop.'

'But the fisherman is sorry,' said the priest. 'He wants to come and live in our temple. He's going to work for us.'

'So our story has a happy ending,' I said.

'Yes, even Bud is happy,' Sue said. 'He has a new idea. He's going to bring all his Buddhas to Thailand. He's going to build a museum for them. He's going to call the museum BUD'S BUDDHAS.'

'That's a good idea,' I said. 'And this is a good story. I'm going to write it down. I'm going to make this story into a book. With pictures. Perhaps you can help me, Sue?'

'That's a good idea, too,' said Sue.

She smiled at me. It was a nice, friendly smile. The priest smiled too. And of course, the Buddha smiled! A strange Buddhist smile.

I like Thailand. They call it the Land of Smiles.

STORY POINTS

Chapter 1
1 Where is Tinker from? What does he do?
2 Where is Sue from? What does she do?
3 What does Tinker see in the cave?
4 What happened to the old Buddha?

Chapter 2
5 Who is Bud with when Tinker sees him? Where does Bud go?
6 Where is Tinker going to stay tonight?
7 What does Tinker see at Lee's Cabana?

Chapter 3
8 Why didn't Tinker sleep well?
9 What does Tinker see in the cabin of the white boat?
10 Why can't Lee take Tinker to the island?

Chapter 4
11 Why does Tinker want to go to the island?
12 How does Sue help him?
13 How do Tinker and Sue get back from the fishing village?

Chapter 5
14 How does the fisherman frighten Tinker out at sea? How does he frighten Tinker on the island?
15 What does the fisherman do on the island? Why?
16 Why does Tinker swim out to sea? What does he see there?

Chapter 6
17 Why does Lee throw the fishing net over Tinker's head?
18 Why did Sue follow Lee?
19 Who saves Tinker? How?

Chapter 7
20 Who stole the Buddha? Why?
21 Where is Lee now? Why?
22 What is Tinker going to do at the end of this story?

Thinking over the story
What can you remember about these people, places and things?
Tinker Sue Bud Lee the fisherman the temple
Lee's Cabana Crab Island the fishing village Bud's yacht
Lee's boat Sue's uncle's boat the fisherman's boat